Wolfgang Amadeus Mozart

2 Serenades

Eine kleine Nachtmusik K 525

Edited by / Herausgegeben von
Dieter Rexroth

Serenade a 8 K 388 ('Nacht Musique')

Edited by / Herausgegeben von
Harry Newstone

Urtext

EULENBURG

EAS 134
ISBN 978-3-7957-6534-7
ISMN M-2002-2358-3

Urtext edition based on Eulenburg Study Score ETP 218 and ETP 309

Ernst Eulenburg Ltd
48 Great Marlborough Street
London W1F 7BB

Contents / Inhalt

Serenade a 8 ('Nacht Musique')

Preface

Eine kleine Nachtmusik K 525

Composed: 1787 in Vienna
First performance: unknown
Original publisher: Johann André, Offenbach, ca.1827
Instrumentation: 2 violins, viola, violoncello e basso
Duration: ca. 18 minutes

The Serenade in G major K 525, *Eine kleine Nachtmusik*, is one of the best-known and best-loved works of Wolfgang Amadeus Mozart and is also one of the most popular pieces of 'classical' music in general. It is Mozart's last contribution to the 'serenade' genre with which he had for a time been so involved. The Salzburg Serenades of the 1770's are functional (*Gebrauchsmusik*), owing their existence, without exception, to specific events and circumstances, but this did not prevent Mozart from attaching increasing artistic value to this music. The three 'big' wind serenades which he composed in Vienna between 1781 and 1782 mark an unmistakable break with the realms of socially orientated entertainment. The 'serenade' assumes the characteristics of chamber music and aspires to its greater artistic demands.

Mozart's Serenade K 525 marks the final retreat and decline of the traditional instrumental serenade. It is the product of an artistic and stylistic awareness which, to use the language of the times, 'lays claim to a quite specialized and sustained character' and which attempts to achieve the unified and integrated structure dictated by the formal principles of the symphony and chamber music. If Mozart's earlier serenades were characterized by a juxtaposition or intermingling of contrasted instrumental groups and by the tensions created by the resulting diversity of sound and colour, in the *Kleine Nachtmusik* Mozart rejected such tensions in favour of a highly subtle differentiation within the homogeneous string group. He in fact employed a greater number of string instruments in the *Kleine Nachtmusik* and did away with the wind section on which, as open-air music, the serenade had always depended. The refined nature of this work indicates the distance at which it stands from the old type of serenade which, being functional music, could not cope with sophisticated compositional techniques because they would have detracted from it as entertainment.

Even if many of the features of the 'old' serenade are no longer apparent, in Mozart's *Kleine Nachtmusik* one cannot fail to recognise the close relationship the overall musical sound bears to the traditional serenade. The impression is of something simple, entertaining and in fact undemanding. Yet this effect is achieved by means of the greatest possible artistic skill and understanding. There is nothing extraneous or superfluous. The form, while showing an extravagant melodic richness, is concisely and clearly delineated. Throughout, the hallmark of this last Mozart Serenade is a matchless perfection and mastery; it was to be followed the next year (1788) by the Divertimento in E flat major K 563 in which the composer finally made it clear that for him traditional socially orientated music together with its peculiar demands was no longer valid.

Despite its unquestioned accomplishment, this work nevertheless presents us with a few puzzles. We know that the *Kleine Nachtmusik* was written in 1787 – the year in which Mozart's father died and, above all, the year of *Don Giovanni*. But we do not know the reason for its composition, nor do we have any clues as to whether the work was performed during Mozart's own lifetime and, if so, when. In addition, the work as we know it is certainly not in its original form. It is clear from Mozart's own handwritten catalogue, the *Verzeichnis aller meiner Werke*, which includes all his compositions from February 1784 on, that the piece originally had five movements, not four. On 10 August Mozart noted 'Eine kleine NachtMusick, consisting of an Allegro, Minuet and Trio, Romance, Minuet and Trio, and Finale. – 2 violini, viola e bassi'.

Thus, as was usual in the serenade form of Mozart's day, the first version of the work contained two minuets and trios – there was originally a Minuet and Trio inserted between the Allegro and the Romance. Has it been lost – or even forcibly removed? We do not know. The accuracy of Mozart's entry in his catalogue can be confirmed by the autograph score. In the sequence of eight rectangular and uncut pages, numbered in Mozart's own hand, page 3 is missing. It occupies precisely the space between the Allegro and the Romance and must therefore have contained the missing first Minuet.

The handwritten score was found amongst Mozart's estate, which was acquired in January 1800 by the publisher and great admirer of Mozart, Johann Anton André of Offenbach. The first edition of the instrumental parts, based on the autograph score, appeared in 1827. It bore the title 'Serenade' but consisted of only four movements – whereas the catalogue published by André in 1805 identifies five movements (see above). It is probably that in spite of the conscientiousness of the publisher, he had acquired the manuscript without page 3. After André's death, his collection was divided up between his sons and sons-in-law with the result that a considerable amount of material of interest to the public vanished. The *Kleine Nachtmusik* was thought for many decades to be lost without trace. Breitkopf & Härtel were not able to use it as source material in their 1883 Mozart Complete Edition nor could it be used for any subsequent editions. In 1943 it was found again by Manfred Gorke in a private collection. Stored temporarily by Bärenreiter in Kassel, it is now once again in private hands.

The discovery of the manuscript made it possible for the edition that appeared in the New Mozart Complete Edition, published by the Internationale Stiftung Mozarteum, to be based on this source. In 1956 the work was issued by Ernst Fritz Schmid as an *Urtext* and in 1955 Bärenreiter brought out a facsimile of the handwritten score. The autograph is executed with the utmost care; it is remarkable for its lively quality and is very beautiful to look at. It shows no signs of any correction and bears typically Mozartian features. The present edition of the score is based on the autograph text – the only important source.

Dieter Rexroth (adapted)
Translation: Penelope Souster

Serenade a 8 K 388 ('Nacht Musique')

Composed: 1782 in Vienna
First performance: unknown
Original publisher: Johann André, Offenbach, 1811
Instrumentation: 2 oboes, 2 clarinets, 2 horns, 2 bassoons
Duration: ca. 23 minutes

On 23 January 1782 Mozart, in a letter to his father, Leopold, reported that Prince Liechtenstein 'would like to collect a wind-instrument band (though he does not yet want it to be known), for which I should write the music.' In April of that year the Emperor (Joseph II) established an official wind band of eight players to perform on public occasions and at court functions. Wind ensembles (*Harmonie*) so constituted were not entirely new in Vienna and elsewhere, but the Emperor's example prompted other members of the aristocracy (the Princes Esterházy and Lobkowitz among them) to form similar groups and, perhaps of greater importance, added impetus for itinerant musicians to take their music into the streets, courtyards and other public places in Vienna. Mozart, himself, had written to Leopold on 3 November 1781 that on his nameday (31 October):

'At 11 o'clock at night I was treated to a serenade [Mozart uses the term *NachtMusick*] performed by two clarinets, two horns and two bassoons – and that too of my own composition – […]. Well, these musicians asked that the street door might be opened and, placing themselves in the centre of the courtyard, surprised me, just as I was about to undress, in the most pleasant fashion imaginable with the first chord in E flat.'

The work in question was what has come to be known as the Serenade in E flat, K 375 in its original sextet version, later amplified to the octet in which form it is now best known.

On 27 July 1782, Mozart again wrote to Leopold: '[…] I have had to compose in a great hurry a serenade [Mozart here uses the form *Nacht Musique*], but only for wind instruments.' He does not say for whom it is being written but, with the Prince Liechtenstein's projected wind band (by now already in existence) as well as the Emperor's recently formed ensemble in mind, there seems to have been sufficient compulsion for Mozart to produce a work for wind octet and it was long thought that he was here referring to the C minor Serenade, but since it had to be produced in 'a great hurry', it seems just as (if not more) likely that he should turn to the above-mentioned already existing sextet and convert it into an octet. This commission apart, it might also be observed that the idiom of the C minor Serenade, more serious and learned than that which Mozart generally employed in his serenades, suggests a formal rather than *al fresco* setting for its performance, which theory may perhaps be supported by the fact that he chose this work to transcribe for string quartet (K 406) in 1787 when he needed to make up a set of three quintets to sell by subscription (together with K 515 and K 516).

The autograph score of the C minor Serenade, upon which single authentic source this new edition is based, is in the Staatsbibliothek zu Berlin – Preußischer Kulturbesitz, Musikabteilung. It is written on 12-stave oblong (landscape) format manuscript paper at the head of which Mozart wrote 'Serenada' over an earlier title 'Parthia', revealed by ultraviolet photography. Further to the right, also in the composer's hand, 'di Wolfgango Amadeo Mozartmp / 1782' below which the date is repeated, probably in the hand of Georg Nikolaus Nissen (Constanze's second husband). The last page of the score (bars 230–252) is not in Mozart's hand and has some questionable and confusing phrasing. We have attempted to bring order to these passages and to the final chord which seems rather oddly distributed among the instruments and which lacks the third. For some clarification of these matters we have (like the editors of the *Neue Mozart-Ausgabe*) examined the string quintet transcription (K 406) of the relevant bars and our revisions may be seen in the main musical text.

Harry Newstone (adapted)

Vorwort

Eine kleine Nachtmusik KV 525

komponiert: 1787 in Wien
Uraufführung: nicht bekannt
Originalverlag: Johann André, Offenbach, ca. 1827
Orchesterbesetzung: 2 Violinen, Viola, Violoncello e Basso
Spieldauer: etwa 18 Minuten

Die Serenade *Eine kleine Nachtmusik* in G-Dur KV 525 zählt zu den bekanntesten und beliebtesten Werken Wolfgang Amadeus Mozarts und zu den volkstümlichsten Werken der „klassischen" Musik überhaupt. Es ist Mozarts letzter Beitrag zur Gattung der „Serenade", die ihn zeitweilig stark beansprucht hatte. Die Salzburger Serenaden der 1770er Jahre sind Gebrauchsmusiken; ihre Entstehung verdankt sich durchweg bestimmten Anlässen und Aufträgen. Das hinderte Mozart nicht, mit dieser Musik einen ständig wachsenden Kunstanspruch zu verbinden. Die drei „großen" Bläserserenaden, die Mozart 1781/82 in Wien komponierte, markieren unverkennbar die Loslösung aus der gesellschaftlichen Unterhaltungssphäre. Die „Serenade" übernimmt die Züge der Kammermusik und geht schließlich in deren hohen Kunstanspruch auf.

Mozarts Serenade KV 525 unterstreicht dann noch einmal und letztmalig die Auflösung und Überwindung des traditionellen instrumentalen Serenadentypus. Sie ist von einem Stil- und Kunstbewusstsein getragen, das „Anspruch auf einen festbestimmten und durchgehaltenen Charakter" erhebt, um in der Sprache der Zeit zu sprechen, und eine Geschlossenheit und Einheit der Gestaltung anstrebt, die von den Form- und Bildungsgesetzlichkeiten der Sinfonie und der Kammermusik her bestimmt werden. War die frühere Serenade Mozarts dadurch gekennzeichnet, dass die Instrumentengruppen kontrastierend gegeneinander gesetzt oder gemischt wurden, was zu vielfältigen Klang- und Farbspannungen führte, so verzichtet Mozart in der *Kleinen Nachtmusik* gerade auf diese Spannungsdimension, um diesen Verzicht allerdings wettzumachen durch ein Höchstmaß an Differenziertheit der Gestaltung innerhalb des homogenen Streicherensembles. Mozart verwendet in der *Kleinen Nachtmusik* eben nur mehr Streicher und verzichtet auf die Bläser, an deren Verwendung ursprünglich die Serenade als Freiluftmusik engstens gebunden war. Der sublime Klangcharakter dieses Werks bezeichnet treffend den Abstand vom Typus der „alten" Serenade, die als Gebrauchsmusik keine kompositorischen Raffinessen und Komplikationen enthalten durfte, da hierdurch nur der Unterhaltungscharakter geschmälert worden wäre.

Auch wenn viele Merkmale der „alten“ Serenade in Mozarts *Kleiner Nachtmusik* aufgehoben erschienen, so bleibt doch unüberhörbar, dass der musikalische Tonfall dieser Musik durchaus noch dem der traditionellen Serenade nahe steht. Alles an der *Kleinen Nachtmusik* wirkt einfach, unterhaltend und eigentlich nicht anspruchsvoll. Doch gerade diese Wirkung ist Resultat höchsten Kunstverstandes und größter Kunstfertigkeit. Auf jeden äußeren Effekt wird verzichtet. Die Form zeigt bei einer verschwenderischen melodischen Fülle klare und konzise Umrisse. Von jeher bilden unübertreffbare Meisterschaft und Vollkommenheit die Etikette dieser letzten Mozartschen Serenade, der der Komponist im folgenden Jahr 1788 noch das Divertimento in Es-Dur KV 563 folgen ließ, um damit endgültig zu bekunden, dass für ihn die traditionelle Gesellschaftsmusik mit ihren spezifischen Ansprüchen keine Gültigkeit mehr hatte.

Ungeachtet der nie in Zweifel gezogenen Vollendetheit gibt dieses Werk doch einige Rätsel auf. Wir wissen, dass die *Kleine Nachtmusik* 1787 komponiert wurde, also in dem Jahr, in dem der Vater starb und dann vor allem der *Don Giovanni* entstand. Den Anlass der Entstehung kennen wir allerdings nicht; ebenso wenig besitzen wir Anhaltspunkte darüber, ob und wann die Komposition zu Lebzeiten Mozarts aufgeführt wurde. Außerdem ist uns das Werk in einer Fassung überliefert, die mit Sicherheit nicht der ursprünglichen entspricht. Aus Mozarts eigenhändigem Werkverzeichnis, das *Verzeichnis all meiner Werke*, seiner sämtlichen Kompositionen ab Februar 1784 geht zweifelsfrei hervor, dass die Komposition in ihrer Originalversion fünf und nicht nur vier Sätze hatte. Unter dem Datum 10. August notierte Mozart: „Eine kleine NachtMusick, bestehend in einem Allegro. Menuett und Trio. – Romanze. Menuett und Trio, und Finale. – 2 violini, viola e bassi.“

Wie für den Typus der Mozartschen Serenade üblich, enthielt das Werk in seiner originalen Fassung also zwei Menuette mit Trios, war ursprünglich zwischen Allegro und Romanze ein Menuett mit Trio eingeschaltet. Ist es verloren gegangen oder gar gewaltsam herausgetrennt worden? Wir wissen es nicht. Bestätigt wird die Richtigkeit von Mozarts Eintragung in seinem Werkverzeichnis durch das Autograph der Partitur. In der Folge der von Mozart eigenhändig paginierten acht querformatigen und unbeschnittenen Blätter fehlt das Blatt 3. Es füllt genau den Platz zwischen dem Allegro und der Romanze, muss also das verloren gegangene erste Menuett enthalten haben.

Die handschriftliche Partitur befand sich in Mozarts Nachlass, den im Januar 1800 der Verleger und große Mozart-Verehrer Johann Anton André aus Offenbach erwarb. 1827 erfolgte der Erstdruck der Stimmen, dem das Autograph zugrunde lag. Die Ausgabe trug den Vermerk „Serenade“, enthielt aber nur vier Sätze, während das im Jahre 1805 von André veröffentlichte Werkverzeichnis tatsächlich fünf Sätze auswies (siehe oben). Bei der Gewissenhaftigkeit des Verlegers ist es wahrscheinlich, dass er das Partiturmanuskript ohne Blatt 3 übernommen hat. Nach Andrés Tod wurde seine Sammlung unter seine Söhne und Schwiegersöhne aufgeteilt, was zur Folge hatte, dass vieles aus den Augen der interessierten Öffentlichkeit verschwand. Auch die *Kleine Nachtmusik* galt viele Jahrzehnte lang als verschollen. Sie lag als Quelle weder der Mozart-Gesamtausgabe bei Breitkopf & Härtel von 1883 noch allen weiteren Ausgaben zugrunde. 1943 fand dann Manfred Gorke das Manuskript in

Privatbesitz wieder. Zeitweilig im Bärenreiter-Verlag in Kassel aufbewahrt, befindet sich die Handschrift heute wieder in Privatbesitz.

Die Wiederauffindung der Handschrift machte es möglich, die Edition im Rahmen der Neuen Mozart-Gesamtausgabe, herausgegeben von der Internationalen Stiftung Mozarteum, an dieser Quelle zu orientieren. Das Werk wurde 1956 von Ernst Fritz Schmid als Urtext-ausgabe vorgelegt. Daneben brachte der Bärenreiter-Verlag 1955 einen Faksimile-Druck der Handschrift heraus. Die Handschrift ist mit größter Sorgfalt angefertigt und zeigt eine bemerkenswerte lebendige Schönheit. Sie weist keine Korrekturen auf und bietet die für Mozart typischen Merkmale. Die nachstehende Ausgabe der Partitur stützt sich auf den Text des Autographs, das die einzig wichtige Quelle darstellt.

Dieter Rexroth (neu bearbeitet)

Serenade a 8 KV 388 („Nacht Musique")

komponiert: 1782 in Wien
Uraufführung: nicht bekannt
Originalverlag: Johann André, Offenbach, 1811
Orchesterbesetzung: 2 Oboen, 2 Klarinetten, 2 Hörner, 2 Fagotte
Spieldauer: etwa 23 Minuten

Am 23. Januar 1782 schrieb Mozart in einem Brief an seinen Vater Leopold: „der Junge fürst Liechstenstein,|:er will es aber noch nicht wissen lassen:| dieser will eine Harmonie Musik aufnehmen, zu welcher ich die stücke setzen soll". Im April desselben Jahres gründete der Kaiser (Joseph II.) ein offizielles Bläserensemble, dessen acht Musiker sowohl bei Hof zur Unterhaltung als auch bei öffentlichen Anlässen aufzuspielen hatten. Solcherart bestallte Bläsergruppen (Harmonien) waren weder in Wien noch anderswo völlig neu, aber das Vorbild des Kaisers veranlasste andere Mitglieder der Aristokratie (u. a. die Fürsten Esterházy und Lobkowitz), ähnliche Bläserensembles zu bilden, und gab – was wohl noch wichtiger war – herumziehenden Wandermusikern einen zusätzlichen Anstoß, ihre Musik auf den Straßen, Innenhöfen und öffentlichen Plätzen Wiens vorzutragen. Mozart selbst hatte am 3. November 1781 an Leopold geschrieben, an seinem Namenstag (31. Oktober) sei Folgendes geschehen:

„… auf die Nacht um 11 uhr bekamm ich eine NachtMusick von 2 clarinetten, 2 Horn, und 2 Fagott – und zwar von meiner eigenen komposition. […] – die Herrn also haben sich die hausthüre öfnen lassen, und nachdemm sie sich mitten im Hof rangirt, mich, da ich mich eben entkleiden wollte, mit dem Ersten E B accord auf die angenehmste art von der Welt überrascht."

Das betreffende Werk ist inzwischen in der Originalfassung für Sextett als Es-Dur-Serenade, KV 375, bekannt, später wurde das Werk zum Oktett erweitert und wird heute meist in dieser Form gespielt.

Am 27. Juli 1782 schrieb Mozart wieder an seinen Vater: „[…] ich habe geschwind eine *Nacht Musique* machen müssen, aber nur auf harmonie“. Zwar erwähnt er nicht, für wen das Werk gedacht ist, aber im Hinblick auf Fürst Liechtensteins geplante (oder vielleicht bereits bestehende) Bläsergruppe und das neue Ensemble des Kaisers gab es für Mozart sicher zwingende Gründe, ein Werk für Bläseroktett zu schreiben, und lange wurde angenommen, dass er sich in diesem Brief auf die c-Moll-Serenade bezog. Da das Werk jedoch „geschwind“ gebraucht wurde, ist genauso gut oder noch eher möglich, dass Mozart das oben erwähnte, bereits bestehende Sextett zum Oktett ausbaute. Abgesehen von der Möglichkeit eines Kompositionsauftrages fällt auch auf, dass der Stil der c-Moll-Serenade – ernster und anspruchsvoller als der von Mozart üblicherweise in seinen Serenaden benutzte – eher auf einen offiziell-formellen Anlass als auf eine ungezwungene Freiluftaufführung schließen lässt. Auch die Tatsache, dass er gerade dieses Werk zur Umarbeitung wählte, als er 1787 für eine Subskriptionsausgabe von drei Streichquintetten (KV 406 – zusammen mit KV 515 und KV 516) Material brauchte, spricht für diese Hypothese.

Das Partiturautograph der c-Moll-Serenade befindet sich in der Staatsbibliothek zu Berlin – Preußischer Kulturbesitz, Musikabteilung mit Mendelssohnarchiv. Die vorliegende Neuausgabe basiert auf dieser einzigen eigenschriftlichen Quelle. Es steht auf Manuskriptpapier in Querformat mit jeweils 12 Systemen. Wie mit Hilfe ultravioletter Fotografie enthüllt wurde, überschrieb Mozart den früheren Titel „Parthia“ mit „Serenada“. Weiter rechts steht, ebenfalls in Mozarts Hand, „di Wolfgango Amadeo Mozartmp / 1782“, dieses Datum steht darunter nochmal – vermutlich in der Hand Georg Nikolaus Nissens (Constanzes zweiter Mann). Die letzte Partiturseite (T. 230–252) ist nicht in Mozarts Hand und enthält einige fragwürdige und ungereimte Phrasierungen. Wir haben versucht, diese Stellen zu bereinigen – auch den letzten Akkord, der etwas seltsam auf die Instrumente verteilt ist und bei dem die Terz fehlt. Zur Klärung dieser Problemstellen haben wir (wie die Herausgeber der *Neuen Mozart-Ausgabe*) die entsprechenden Takte der Quintettübertragung (KV 406) konsultiert und unsere editorische Fassung in den Notentext integriert.

Harry Newstone (neu bearbeitet)
Übersetzung: Judith Meier

Eine kleine Nachtmusik

Wolfgang Amadeus Mozart
(1756–1791)
K 525

I. Allegro

24
29
34
40
45

50
56
62
68
74

tr
p
sf
cresc.
f

109
tr
f
3
115
p
f
121
tr
126
p
132

II. Romance

Andante
Violino
I
II
Viola
Violoncello
e Contrabbasso
p
f
tr
cresc.
fp

21
24
27
31
35
tr
f

39
[p]
[p]
[p]
[p]
41
fp
fp
fp
fp
44
47
50
[p]
[p]
p

54
58
61
cresc.
cresc.
cresc.
cresc.
65
69

III. Menuetto

IV. Rondo

Allegro

26
31
36
42
f
f
f
f
47
p
p
p
p

52
1
2
f
56
p
62
67
72

77
82
sf
p
87
93
99

105
111
117
123
129
Coda

135
141
tr
147
152
158
f

Serenade a 8 ('Nacht Musique')

Wolfgang Amadeus Mozart
(1756–1791)
K 388

I. Allegro

Ob.
Cl. (B♭)
Cor. (E♭)
Fg.
a 2
f
p
tr
Ob. 1
Cl. (B♭)
Fg. 1
[a 2]
calando
[calando]
calando
calando

Ob.
Cl. (B♭)
Cor. (E♭)
Fg.
dolce
2.

46
Ob. 1
Cl. (B♭)
Cor. (E♭)
Fg.
Solo
52
Ob.
Cl. (B♭)
Cor. (E♭)
Fg.

58
Ob.
Cl. (B♭)
Cor. (E♭)
Fg.
1.
64
f
69

Ob.
Cl. (B♭)
Cor. (E♭)
Fg.

89
Ob.
Cl. (B♭)
Cor. (E♭)
Fg.
p
sf
sfp
[f]
f
95
dolce
102

109
Ob.
Cl. (B♭)
Cor. (E♭)
Fg.
tr
p
115
f
[simile]
120
[a 2]

125
Ob.
Cl. (B♭)
Cor. (E♭)
Fg.
a 2
p
[f]
131
tr
[a 2]
138
f
[♮]

144
Ob. 1
Cl. (B♭) 1
2
Cor. (E♭) 1 2
Fg. 1
tr
p
151
Ob. 1
2
Cl. (B♭) 1
2
Cor. (E♭) 1 2
[a 2]
Fg. 1
2
f
156
[a 2]

161
Ob.
Cl. (B♭)
Cor. (E♭)
a 2
Fg.
f
p
sf
167
174

180
Ob.
Cl. (B♭)
Cor. (E♭)
Fg.
p
186

191
Ob.
Cl. (B♭)
Cor. (E♭)
Fg.
196
Ob.
Cl. (B♭)
Cor. (E♭)
Fg.

201
Ob.
Cl. (B♭)
Cor. (E♭)
Fg.
206
211

216
Ob.
Cl. (B♭)
Cor. (E♭)
Fg.
221
226

II. Andante

Oboe
1
2
Clarinetto (B♭)
1
2
Corno (E♭) 1 2
Fagotto
1
2
p dolce
sfp

11
Ob.
1
2
Cl. (B♭)
1
2
Cor. (E♭) 1 2
Fg.
1
2
sfp

19
Ob.
Cl. (B♭)
Cor. (E♭)
Fg.
[a 2]
27
cresc.
f
33

38
Ob.
Cl. (B♭)
Cor. (E♭)
Fg.
43
53
p
[p]
sfp
cresc.
[2.]

64
Ob.
Cl. (B♭)
Cor. (E♭)
Fg.
p dolce
p [dolce]
[p dolce]
sfp
75
83
2.

90
Ob.
1
2
Cl. (B♭)
cresc.
Cor. (E♭)
Fg.
f
95
p
[p]
101
pp

III. Menuetto in canone

17
Ob.
Cl. (B♭)
Cor. (E♭)
Fg.
p
sfp
fp
f
27
tr
35
a 2

Ob.
Cl. (B♭)
Cor. (E♭)
Fg.
a 2
Trio in canone al roverscio
a mezza voce
Menuetto da capo

IV. Allegro

17
Ob.
1
2
Cl. (B♭)
1
2
Cor. (E♭)
1
2
Fg.
1
2
22

27
Ob.
1
2
Cl. (B♭)
Cor. (E♭)
Fg.
[Solo]
33
p
41

49
Ob.
Cl. (B♭)
Fg.
p
pp
[p]
[pp]
57
65
Cor. (E♭)
f
tr

74
Ob.
Cl. (B♭)
Cor. (E♭)
Fg.
80
89

95
Ob.
Cl. (B♭)
Cor. (E♭)
Fg.
106
115
[p]

126
Ob.
Cl. (B♭)
Cor. (E♭)
Fg.
mfp
fp
[p]
135
146
[·]

154
Ob.
Cl. (B♭)
Fg.
161
168
174
pp
mfp

187
Ob.
Cl. (B♭)
Fg.
mfp
sfp
fp
200
Cor. (E♭)
[p]
214
f

Printed in China

THE ART OF SCORE-READING

The first steps

A score contains the entire musical text of a musical work in order that the conductor and everyone who wants to study the piece more thoroughly can see exactly which passages are being played by the orchestra or ensemble. The parts of the individual instruments are arranged in such a way that all notes played at the same time are written one below the other.
Scores help to listen to, understand and interpret musical works. Those who only listen to music are unaware of many important details which, after some practice, become apparent when reading the score while listening to the music. The clear structure of the score helps to easily understand the compositional style and the characteristic features of a piece – this is a prerequisite not only for any analysis but also for the musician's own performance and interpretation.

The simplest method of score-reading is to read an individual part by concentrating on an individual part that can be heard particularly well. The most suitable pieces to begin with are concertos with solo instruments such as Beethoven's Romance in F major for violin and orchestra (example 1) or orchestral songs (with them, one may easily follow the text). Furthermore, in many classical orchestral works, it is quite easy to follow the lead part of the principal violin, or the bass part in baroque compositions for orchestra.

The next step is to try to change from one part to another and vice versa and follow the part that is leading. Little by little, you learn to find distinctive parts you hear in the score as well and follow them in the corresponding staff. This can be very easily tried out with Beethoven's Symphony No. 5 (example 2). To read the score, it is also helpful to count the bars. This technique is rather useful in the case of confusing or complex scores, such as those of contemporary music, and is particularly suitable when you do not want to lag behind in any case. It should be your aim, however, to eventually give up counting the bars and to read the score by first following individual parts and then going over to section-by-section or selective reading (see next page).

Example 1 · from: Romance for violin and orchestra in F major by Beethoven

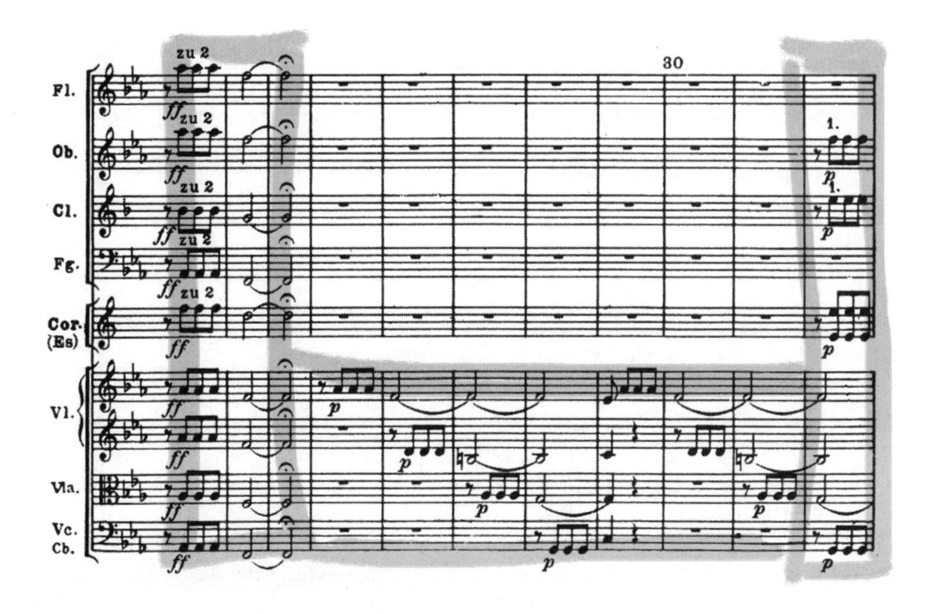

Example 2 · from: Symphony No. 5 C-minor by Beethoven

Further score-reading techniques

Example 3 · from: Symphony No. 100 G major 'Military' by Haydn

Example 4 · from: Symphony No. 41 C major 'Jupiter' by W. A. Mozart

Section-by-section reading

This technique is suitable for application in the 'Military' Symphony by Haydn (example 3). In bb. 260-264, the parts are mostly in parallel motion so that it is quite easy to take in the section as a whole. In the strings, the texture is homophonic (i.e. all instruments play the same rhythm), consisting of tone repetitions in the lower parts while there is a little more movement in the part of the first violin. At the same time, the tones of the winds are stationary (i.e. long sustained notes), serving as harmonic filling-in. If need be, they can also be read en bloc.

Such block-like structures often consist of unison figures (= all instruments play the same), such as at the beginning of Mozart's Jupiter Symphony (example 4). Here, the score-reading can first be limited to the strings section which carries the melody alone in bb. 3-4 and contains all important information.

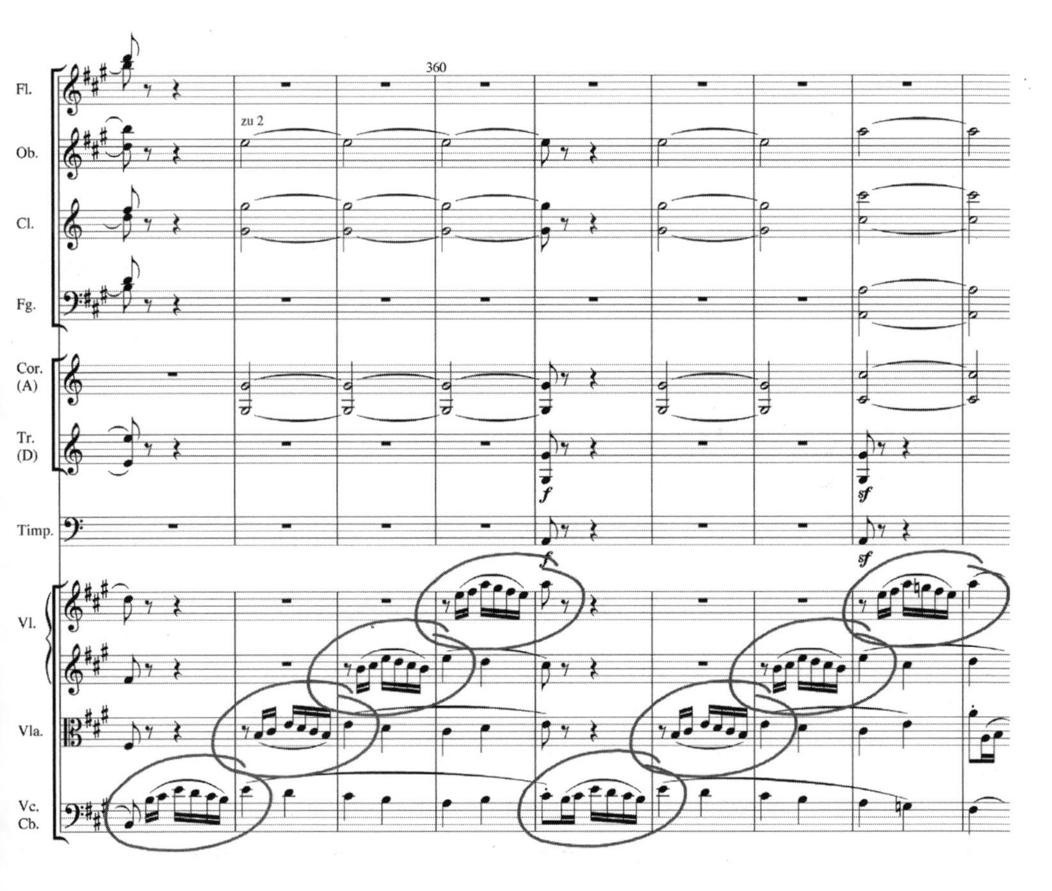

Example 5 · from: Symphony No. 7 A major by Beethoven

Selektive reading

Using this technique, you concentrate on selected parts (lead parts, conspicuous passages) in the score. In the excerpt from Beethoven's Symphony No. 7 (example 5), it is the semiquaver motif that, originating with the violoncellos and basses and pervading the string parts twice, is particularly well suited. The stationary tones of the winds, consisting only of the note E in various octave positions in bb. 358-363, form the harmonic foundation and play a subordinate role in score-reading. Though they are briefly noticed, it is the strings and especially the conspicuous semiquaver motif pervading the individual parts that are to be followed.

With both score-reading techniques which should be chosen according to the nature of the passage in question, it is not important in the beginning to be able to follow at once all tones and harmonies. What matters more is to recognize and comprehend sequences of movement. Everything else comes with experience.

Following contrapuntal parts

The present excerpt from Brahms's Requiem (example 6) is polyphonic, i.e. one has to be able to follow several equal parts either alternately (without lagging behind) or simultaneously. But by looking for parallel parts in the score, the notation which, at first glance, seems to be overcrowded soon becomes clearer. For example, Brahms allocates orchestral parts to each choral part. As a consequence, there are many parts written in the score but considerably fewer independent parts actually played. Hence, the large amount of written music can be reduced to a manageable quantity.

The flute, clarinet, first violins and soprano are in parallel motion. Furthermore, the tenor of oboe and viola is supported by a much-expanded, yet parallel part.
The violoncellos and bassoons too are in almost parallel motion.

The low winds and strings as well as the timpani played simultaneously with the polyphonic parts are fill-in parts which consist only of stationary tones (sustained notes). They do not need to be followed upon first reading of the score.

Seen as a whole, this excerpt is most suitable for focussing on the soprano voice as it is coupled with two instruments and, being the highest voice, can be heard very well. In addition, the text is an aid to orientation, making it easier to return from brief trips to other parts.

In fugal sections, score-reading will be easier if the entries of the theme in the score are first looked for and then marked.

Example 6 · from: A German Requiem by Brahms

The score at a glance

A **Bar lines** are solid vertical lines within the instrument sections.

B The **bar numbers** are an aid to orientation in the score. Sometimes capital letters, so-called rehearsal letters, are used instead of numbers.

C The system of parallel lines on and between which the notes are written is called **staff** (or stave). The instrument abbreviation in front of each line (here, Fl. is for 'flute') indicates to which instrument(s) the line(s) refer(s).

D The **barline at the left-hand end** of the staves connects all staves to form the **system**.

E In addition to the barline at the left-hand end of the staves, **angular brackets** connect the individual groups of instruments in a score (wind, brass and string instruments). Within these groups, the instruments are arranged according to their pitch, with the highest-pitched instrument mentioned first.
Today, the common order of instrumental parts in the score is as follows, from top to bottom:

- wind instruments
- brass instruments
- percussion instruments
- harp, piano, celesta
- solo instrument(s)
- solo voices
- choir
- string instruments

F When there are two systems on a page, they are separated from each other by two parallel **diagonal strokes**.

G Instruments the names of which are followed by 'in Bb' or (Bb) are **transposing instruments**. In this case, (Bb) indicates that the notated C is played as Bb, i.e. all tones are played a tone lower than notated. Most of the transposing instruments are easily recognizable in the score thanks to these additions. However, there are also transposing instruments without such indications in the score, such as:

- piccolo flute (in C / an octave higher)
- cor anglais (in F / a fifth lower)
- contrabassoon (in C / an octave lower)
- double bass (in C / an octave lower)

H The transposing brass instruments have no general signature but, if need be, accidentals preceding the respective tone.

I The viola part is notated in the **alto clef**, the parts of violoncello and bassoon sometimes in the **tenor clef**. Both clefs are easy to read when the player realizes that the clef frames the note C1:

alto clef = tenor clef = treble clef

J Any change of key or time is marked by a **double bar**. The alla-breve sign following in this example (¢), like the sign for four-four time (c), is a relic from an old notational practice and stands for two-two time.

B
A
C
4
29
Fl.
sfp
dim.
pp
D
Ob.
Cl. (B♭)
1.
E
Fag.
Cor. (B♭)
Vl.
I
II
arco
Vla.
Vc.
Cb.
F
34
G
H
Tr. (B♭)
Timp.
ff
tr
cresc.
I
J

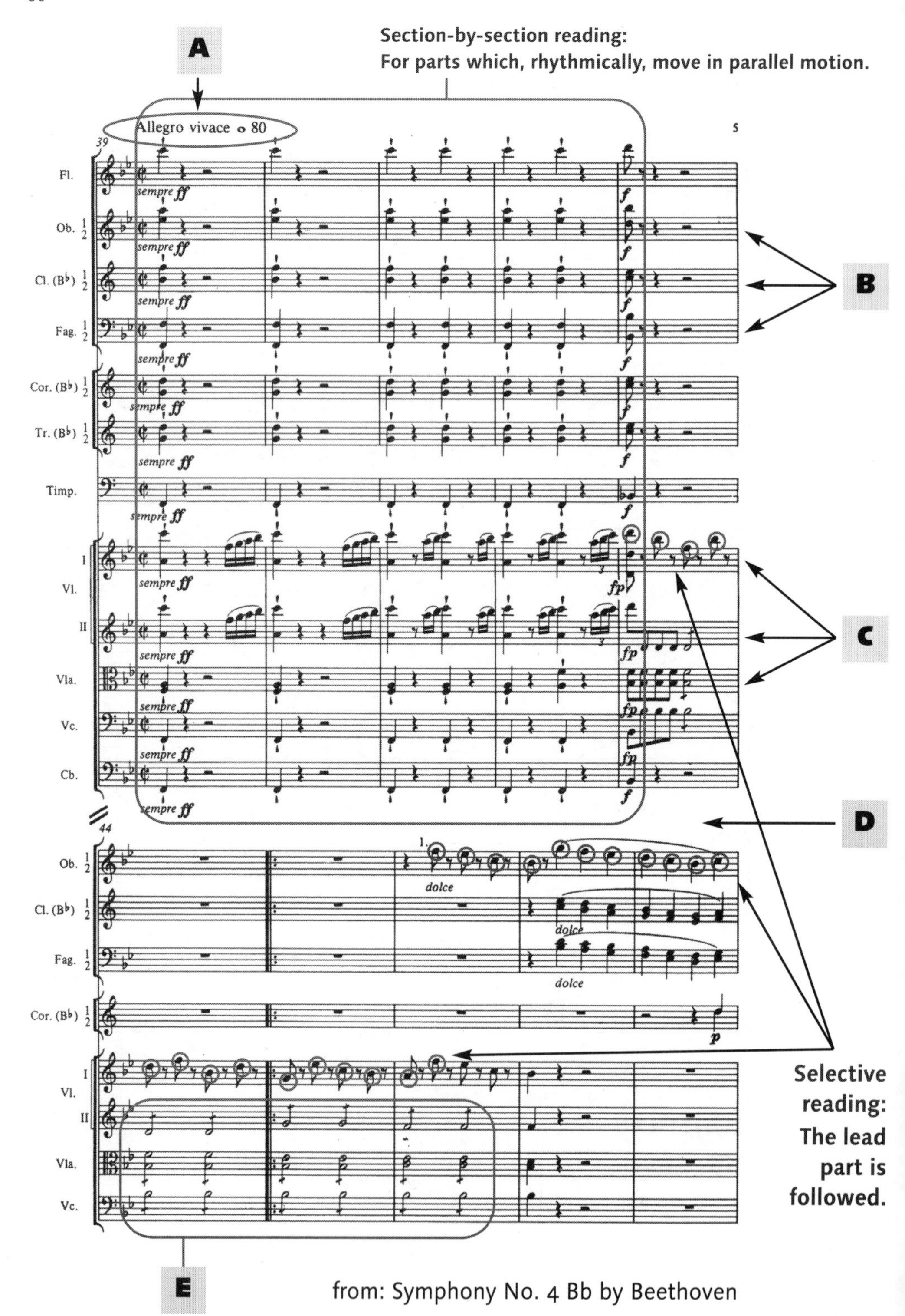

from: Symphony No. 4 Bb by Beethoven

A **Tempo indications** (sometimes in connection with metronome markings) are used by the composer to indicate how fast a piece shall be played.

B In the winds, two parts are usually brought together in one line. If they play the same note, the note head either has two stems or 'a2' written above it.

C Two-part chords in the staves of the strings are played by one player. If the parts shall be divided, **divisi** (divided) is written in the score. Then, at each desk, one player plays the upper notes and another player the lower notes.

D When an instrumental part contains a long rest, as in this flute part for example, its staff is often omitted until the next entry of the instrument, thus saving space. In addition, there are less page-turns, and the playing parts are arranged much clearer.

E In order to save space and arrange phrases or groups of notes more clearly, so-called abbreviations are used occasionally. The sign 𝅗𝅥 stands for ♩♩♩♩, with the minim indicating the duration of the repetitions and the stroke crossing the stem indicating the value of the notes to be repeated (1 stroke = quaver, 2 strokes = semiquaver, etc.). Cf. also the viola in b. 43 in which the repeated notes are first written out and then abbreviated.

DIE KUNST
DES PARTITURLESENS

Der erste Einstieg

Eine Partitur enthält den gesamten Notentext eines Musikwerkes, damit der Dirigent und jeder, der sich näher mit dem Stück beschäftigen will, genau nachvollziehen kann, was das Orchester oder das Ensemble spielt. Dabei sind die Instrumente so angeordnet, dass alle Noten, die zur gleichen Zeit erklingen, genau untereinander stehen. Partituren helfen beim Hören, Begreifen und Interpretieren von Musikliteratur. Wer nur zuhört, erkennt viele kostbare Kleinigkeiten nicht, die beim Mitlesen nach ein wenig Übung regelrecht sichtbar werden. Der Kompositionsstil und die Charakteristik eines Werkes lassen sich mit der übersichtlichen Partitur schnell begreifen – das ist nicht nur Grundvoraussetzung für jede Analyse, sondern auch für das eigene Spiel.

Die einfachste Methode beim Partiturlesen ist das Verfolgen einer Einzelstimme. Bei diesem Verfahren konzentriert man sich auf eine einzelne Stimme, die besonders gut zu hören ist. Zum Einstieg eignen sich dabei besonders gut Konzerte mit Soloinstrumenten wie die Romanze in F-Dur für Violine und Orchester von Beethoven (Beispiel 1) oder Orchesterlieder (bei letzteren kann man sich leicht am Text orientieren). Weiterhin kann man bei vielen klassischen Orchesterwerken die führende Stimme der ersten Violine gut verfolgen, sowie bei barocken Kompositionen für Orchester die Bass-Stimme.

In einem nächsten Schritt kann man versuchen, zwischen den Stimmen zu wechseln und jeweils die Stimme zu verfolgen, die gerade führend ist. Nach und nach lernt man dabei markante Stimmen, die man hört, auch in der Partitur zu finden und im entsprechenden Notensystem zu verfolgen. Besonders anschaulich kann man das mittels Beethovens 5. Symphonie erproben (Beispiel 2).
Eine weitere Hilfe beim Lesen der Partitur kann auch das Mitzählen der Takte sein. Dieses Verfahren hilft bei unübersichtlichen oder komplexen Partituren wie etwa zeitgenössischer Musik und eignet sich besonders, wenn man den Anschluss auf keinen Fall verlieren möchte. Ziel sollte es jedoch sein, das Mitzählen der Takte gänzlich zu verlassen und die Partitur zunächst anhand einzelner Stimmen und dann im Wechsel von blockweisem bzw. selektivem Lesen zu verfolgen (siehe nächste Seite).

Beispiel 1 · aus: Romanze für Violine und Orchester F-Dur von Beethoven

Beispiel 2 · aus: Symphonie Nr. 5 c-moll von Beethoven

Weitere Methoden des Partiturlesens

Beispiel 3 · aus: Symphonie Nr. 100 G-Dur „Militär" von Haydn

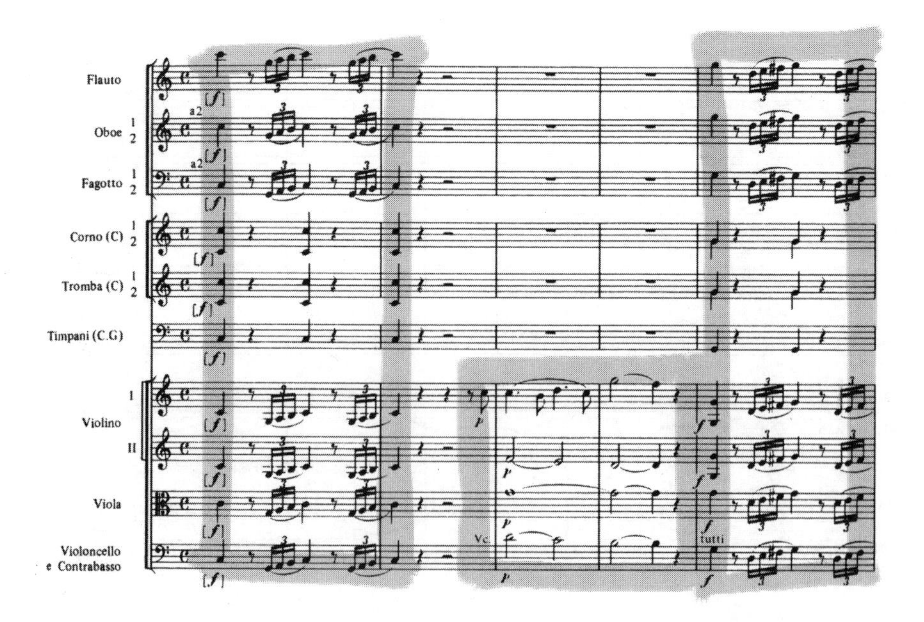

Beispiel 4 · aus: Symphonie Nr. 41 C-Dur „Jupiter" von W. A. Mozart

Blockweises Lesen

Diese Methode bietet sich in der Militär-Symphonie von Haydn an (Beispiel 3). In den T. 260-264 sind die Stimmen weitgehend parallel geführt, so dass man sie gut im Ganzen überblicken kann. In den Streichern haben wir einen homophonen Satz (d.h. alle Stimmen spielen den gleichen Rhythmus), der in den unteren Stimmen aus Tonwiederholungen besteht, während die erste Violine etwas bewegter ist. Gleichzeitig erklingen in den Bläserstimmen Liegetöne (d.h. lang ausgehaltene Töne), die als harmonischer Füllstoff dienen. Sie können bei Bedarf auch im Block gelesen werden.
Oft bestehen solche blockhaften Gebilde auch aus unisono-Figuren (= alle Stimmen spielen dasselbe), wie z.B. am Beginn der Jupiter-Symphonie von Mozart (Beispiel 4). Hier kann man sich beim Lesen zunächst nur auf den Streicherblock beschränken, der in den T. 3-4 alleine die Melodie weiterführt und bereits alle wichtigen Informationen enthält.

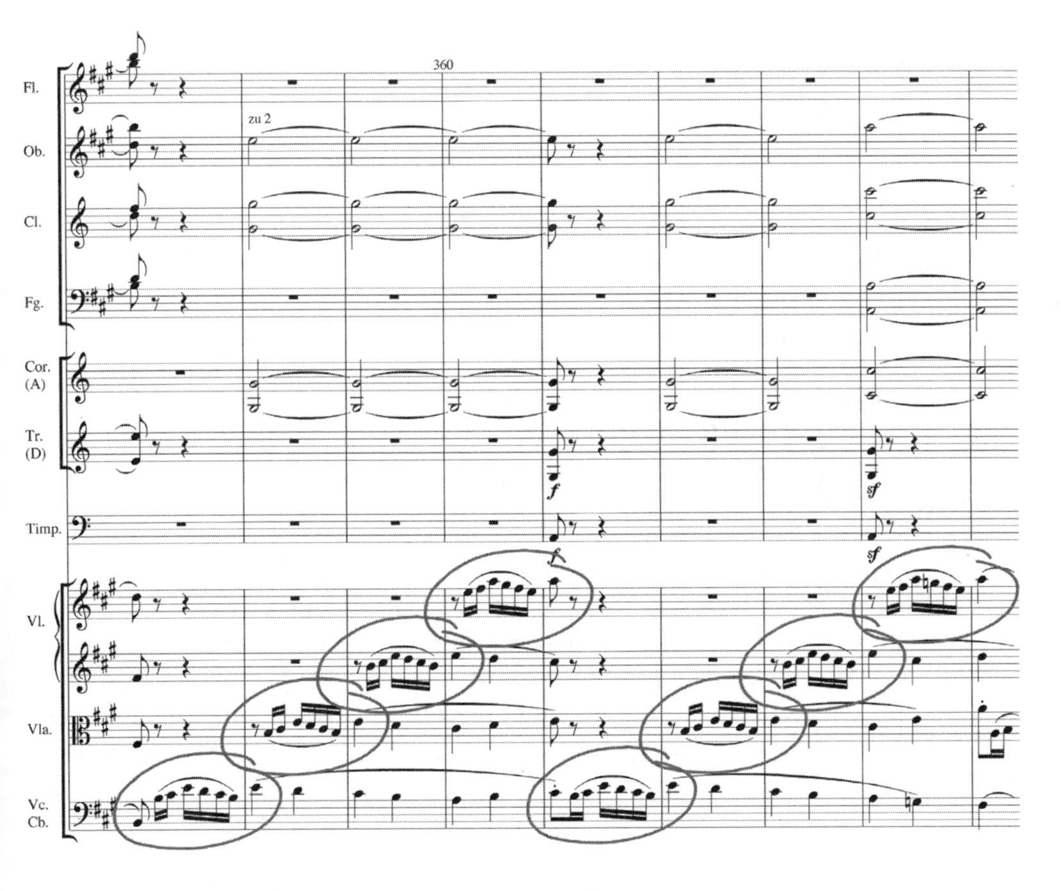

Beispiel 5 · aus: Symphonie Nr. 7 A-Dur von Beethoven

Selektives Lesen

Bei dieser Methode orientiert man sich anhand ausgewählter Stimmen (führende Stimmen, auffällige Stellen) in der Partitur. Im Ausschnitt aus Beethovens 7. Symphonie (Beispiel 5) ist hierzu das Sechzehntelmotiv geeignet, das zweimal von den Celli und Bässen ausgehend durch die Streicherstimmen wandert. Die Liegetöne der Bläser, die in den T. 358-363 sogar nur aus dem Ton e in unterschiedlichen Oktavlagen bestehen, bilden die harmonische Grundierung und spielen beim Lesen der Partitur eine untergeordnete Rolle. Man nimmt sie kurz wahr, verfolgt jedoch die Streicher und dort insbesondere das auffällige Sechzehntelmotiv in seiner Wanderung durch die einzelnen Stimmen.
Bei beiden Leseformen, zwischen denen man übrigens je nach Beschaffenheit der Stelle wechseln sollte, kommt es am Anfang nicht darauf an, sofort alle Töne und Harmonien verfolgen zu können. Viel wichtiger ist es, Bewegungsabläufe zu erkennen und nachzuvollziehen. Alles Weitere kommt mit der Erfahrung.

Verfolgen von kontrapunktischen Stimmen

Der vorliegende Ausschnitt aus Brahms' Requiem (Beispiel 6) ist polyphon komponiert, d.h. man muss mehrere gleichwertige Stimmen entweder im Wechsel (ohne den Anschluss zu verlieren) oder gleichzeitig verfolgen können.
Doch das auf den ersten Blick so übervolle Notenbild lichtet sich bald, wenn man sich die Partitur näher auf parallele Stimmen ansieht. Brahms ordnet z.B. jeder Chorstimme Orchesterstimmen zu. Das hat zur Folge, dass hier zwar viele Stimmen notiert sind, aber wesentlich weniger eigenständige Stimmen tatsächlich erklingen. Die vielen geschriebenen Noten lassen sich also auf ein überschaubares Maß reduzieren.
So werden Flöte, Klarinette, erste Violinen und Sopran parallel geführt. Des Weiteren wird der Tenor von Oboe und Bratsche mit einer stark erweiterten, aber dennoch parallel verlaufenden Stimme unterstützt. Ebenfalls fast ganz parallel verlaufen Violoncelli und Fagotte.
Zu den polyphon gefügten Stimmen erklingen die tiefen Bläser und Streicher sowie die Pauke mit Füllstimmen, welche lediglich aus Liegetönen (ausgehaltene Töne) bestehen. Sie braucht man beim ersten Lesen nicht weiter zu verfolgen.
Im Ganzen gesehen bietet sich in diesem Ausschnitt an, schwerpunktmäßig die Sopranstimme zu verfolgen, da sie mit zwei Instrumenten gekoppelt ist und als höchste Stimme gut herauszuhören ist. Zudem bietet der Text eine Orientierungshilfe, so dass der Wiedereinstieg von vorübergehenden Ausflügen in andere Stimmen erleichtert wird.
Bei fugierten Abschnitten kann man sich das Mitlesen auch erleichtern, indem man zunächst alle Einsätze des Themas in der Partitur sucht und sich markiert.

Beispiel 6 · aus: Ein deutsches Requiem von Brahms

Die Partitur im Überblick

A **Taktstriche** sind innerhalb der Instrumentengruppen durchgezogen.

B Die **Taktzahlen** erleichtern die Orientierung in der Partitur. Manchmal dienen hierzu auch Großbuchstaben, sog. Studierbuchstaben.

C Eine einzelne Zeile der Partitur nennt man **Notensystem**. Für welche(s) Instrument(e) sie steht, zeigt der **Instrumentenvorsatz** an (hier Fl. für Flöte).

D Der **Kopfstrich** verbindet alle Notensysteme miteinander zu einer **Akkolade**.

E Zusätzlich zum Kopfstrich fassen **gerade Klammern** die einzelnen Instrumentengruppen (Holz-, Blech- und Streichinstrumente) zusammen. Innerhalb dieser Gruppen sind die Instrumente nach Tonlage geordnet, wobei das höchste an oberster Stelle steht.
Die heute übliche Partituranordnung lautet von oben nach unten:
· Holzblasinstrumente
· Blechblasinstrumente
· Schlaginstrumente
· Harfe, Klavier, Celesta
· Soloinstrument(e)
· Solostimmen
· Chor
· Streichinstrumente

F Stehen zwei Akkoladen auf einer Seite, werden sie durch zwei **Schrägstriche** voneinander abgetrennt.

G Steht hinter dem Instrumentennamen z.B. „in B" oder (B), handelt es sich um ein **transponierendes Instrument**. In diesem Fall deutet das (B) an, dass das notierte C als B erklingt, also alle Noten einen Ton tiefer erklingen als sie notiert sind. Die meisten transponierenden Instrumente sind in der Partitur durch diese Zusätze leicht zu erkennen. Es gibt aber auch transponierende Instrumente ohne eine entsprechende Angabe in der Partitur, wie z.B.:
Piccoloflöte (in c/eine Oktave höher)
Englischhorn (in f/eine Quinte tiefer)
Kontrafagott (in c/eine Oktave tiefer)
Kontrabass (in c/eine Oktave tiefer)

H Die transponierenden Blechblasinstrumente haben keine Generalvorzeichen, sondern bei Bedarf Versetzungszeichen, die direkt vor der jeweiligen Note stehen.

I Die Viola oder Bratsche wird im **Alt- bzw. Bratschenschlüssel** notiert, die Stimmen des Violoncellos und Fagotts manchmal im **Tenorschlüssel**. Beide Schlüssel sind leicht zu lesen, wenn man sich klarmacht, dass der Schlüssel den Ton c1 umrahmt, also:

Alt- = Tenor- = Violinschlüssel

J Vor einem Wechsel der Ton- oder Taktart steht immer ein **Doppelstrich**. Das hier folgende Alla-Breve-Zeichen (¢) ist ebenso wie das Zeichen für den 4/4-Takt (c) ein Relikt aus einer älteren Notationspraxis und steht für den 2/2-Takt.

A
B
C
D
E
F
G
H
I
J
4
29
34
Fl.
Ob.
Cl. (B♭)
Fag.
Cor. (B♭)
Tr. (B♭)
Timp.
Vl.
I
II
Vla.
Vc.
Cb.
sfp
dim.
pp
arco
ff
cresc.
tr

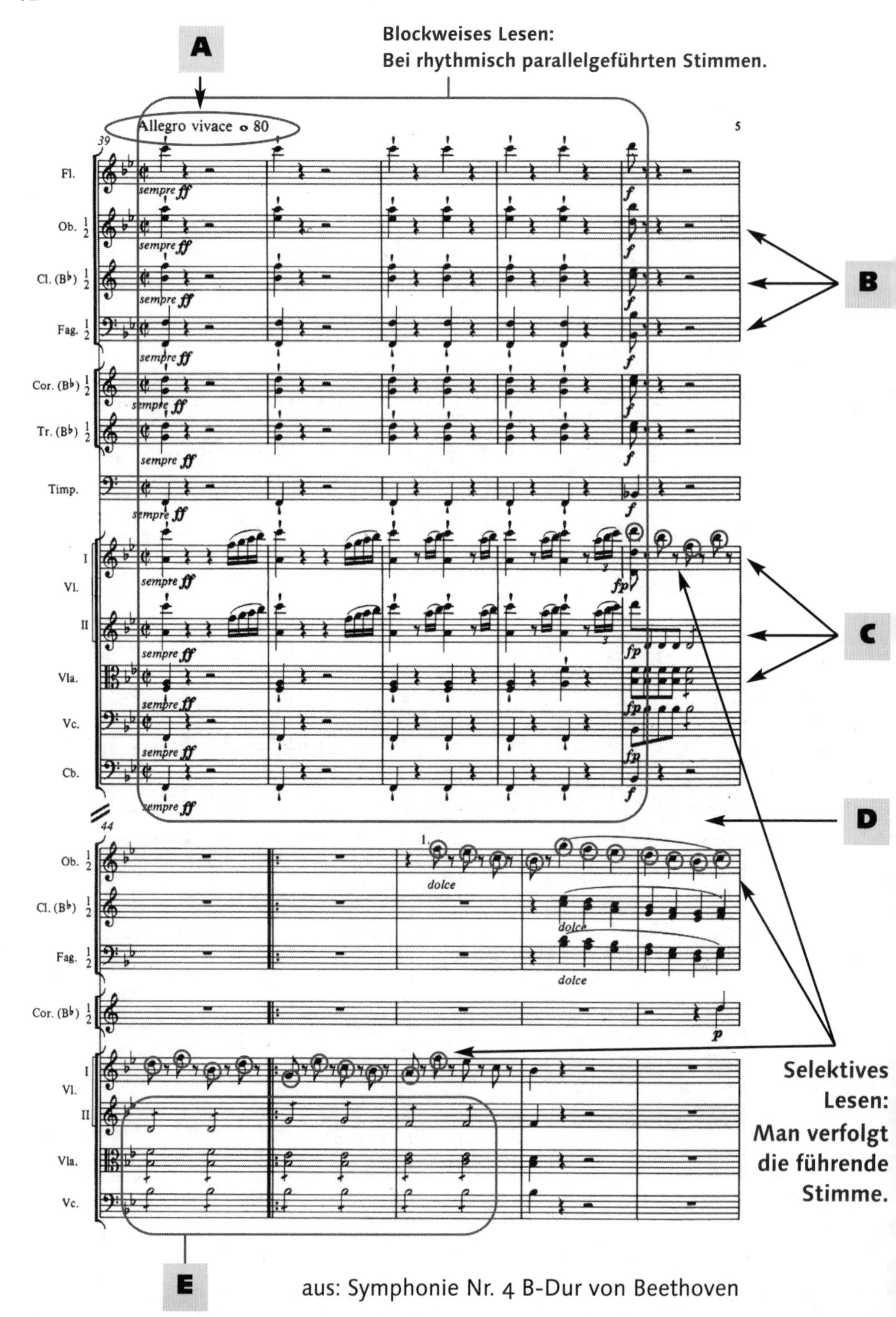

aus: Symphonie Nr. 4 B-Dur von Beethoven

A Durch die **Tempoangabe** (manchmal mit einer Metronomzahl verbunden) gibt der Komponist an, wie schnell ein Stück gespielt werden soll.

B Bei den Bläsern werden in der Regel zwei Stimmen in einer Notenzeile zusammengefasst. Spielen sie den gleichen Ton, erhält der Notenkopf zwei Hälse oder es steht a2 darüber.

C Zweistimmige Akkorde in den Notensystemen der Streicher werden von einem Spieler gespielt. Will man die Stimmen aufteilen, schreibt man **divisi** (geteilt). Dann spielt an jedem Pult ein Spieler die oberen und ein Spieler die unteren Noten.

D Hat eine Stimme, wie hier die Flöte, längere Zeit Pause, wird ihr Notensystem oft bis zum erneuten Einsatz der Stimme weggelassen. So wird Platz gespart, man muß weniger blättern und die erklingenden Stimmen sind übersichtlicher angeordnet.

E Um Platz zu sparen und Tonfolgen übersichtlicher zu gestalten, verwendet man gelegentlich sogenannte **Abbreviaturen (Faulenzer)**. Das hier verwendete Zeichen 𝅗𝅥 steht für ♩♩♩♩, wobei die Halbe Note die Dauer der Wiederholungen anzeigt und der Strich durch den Notenhals den Wert der zu wiederholenden Noten (1 Strich = Achtel, 2 = Sechzehntel usw.). Vgl. auch die Viola in T. 43, in der zunächst die Repetitionen ausgeschrieben und dann abgekürzt sind.